The **Lion** and the **Jackal**

by Tracy Turner-Jones and Maïté Schmitt

FRANKLIN WATTS
LONDON•SYDNEY

Long ago, there lived a jackal.

He was a very clever animal

and he liked to play tricks on Lion.

One day, Jackal went out to look for food. He walked and walked until he came to a path.

The path was rocky and it was very hot.

Jackal was hungry. His tummy rumbled.

"The animals are all hiding from the sun,"

he thought to himself. "But maybe

I will be lucky and find a little lizard or two."

Jackal went on along the path, sniffing

for food. Suddenly he saw something move.

Jackal stopped and looked up. It was Lion!

Jackal had played lots of tricks on Lion before.

"Oh my!" Jackal thought. "Now I'm in trouble.

Lion was coming towards him.

Jackal looked around. There was nowhere to hide. Lion was getting closer. His mouth was open wide.

"He will eat me this time," thought Jackal. "What can I do?"

But then, Jackal had an idea.

He put his paws over his head.

"Watch out, Lion!" he screamed.

Lion stopped, surprised.

Jackal pointed at the rocks above
and howled as loudly as he could.

"Great Lion, please save us!" he cried.

"The big rock is going to fall on our heads."

Lion was puzzled.

"What are you talking about?" he asked.

"The rocks are going to tumble down,"
Jackal cried. "We will be crushed flat
like this!" He lay flat on the ground
to show Lion. "You must save us," he said.

Lion looked up at the rocks.

He didn't know what to do.

Jackal pointed to a big rock.

"Put your strong shoulders here," he said.

So, Lion put his shoulders against the rock
and pushed.

"Now just stay there,' said Jackal.

"I'll go and find a log to hold up the rock.

I'll be back soon."

Jackal ran off as fast as he could.

Lion waited ... and waited.

"Why is Jackal taking so long?" thought Lion.

"Perhaps he can't find a log." He looked

along the valley. Jackal wasn't there.

Slowly, Lion realised what had happened. Jackal wasn't coming back. That clever Jackal had tricked him again!

Jackal ran far from the valley, laughing.

He soon found something very tasty to eat.

"I wonder what trick I can play on Lion

next?" he thought.

Clever Jackal carried on playing tricks

on all the animals. But he always saved

his best ones for Lion.

Story order

Look at these 5 pictures and captions.
Put the pictures in the right order
to retell the story.

1

Lion discovers the tasty-looking Jackal.

2

Jackal runs off, pretending to look for a log.

3

Jackal makes Lion think the rock is falling.

4

Jackal cannot find anything to eat.

5

Lion tries to hold up the rock.

Independent Reading

This series is designed to provide an opportunity for your child to read on their own. These notes are written for you to help your child choose a book and to read it independently.

In school, your child's teacher will often be using reading books which have been banded to support the process of learning to read. Use the book band colour your child is reading in school to help you make a good choice. *The Lion and the Jackal* is a good choice for children reading at Purple Band in their classroom to read independently.

The aim of independent reading is to read this book with ease, so that your child enjoys the story and relates it to their own experiences.

About the book

A jackal is looking for food but a hungry lion soon finds the tasty-looking jackal. Thinking quickly, Jackal tricks Lion into believing a rock is about to fall and crush them. While Lion tries to hold up the rock, Jackal makes his escape.

Before reading

Help your child to learn how to make good choices by asking: "Why did you choose this book? Why do you think you will enjoy it?" Look at the cover together and ask: "What do you think the story will be about?" Ask your child to think of what they already know about the story context. Then ask your child to read the title aloud. Ask: "Describe what the jackal looks like. Does it remind you of any other animals?" Remind your child that they can sound out the letters to make a word if they get stuck.

Decide together whether your child will read the story independently or read it aloud to you.

During reading

Remind your child of what they know and what they can do independently. If reading aloud, support your child if they hesitate or ask for help by telling the word. If reading to themselves, remind your child that they can come and ask for your help if stuck.

After reading

Support comprehension by asking your child to tell you about the story. Use the story order puzzle to encourage your child to retell the story in the right sequence, in their own words. The correct sequence can be found on the next page.

Give your child a chance to respond to the story: "Does this story remind you of any other stories? How do you think Lion felt at the end of the story?"

Help your child think about the messages in the book that go beyond the story and ask: "How do you think Lion would behave if he met Jackal again?"

Extending learning

Help your child predict other possible outcomes of the story by asking: "If Jackal kept playing tricks, do you think the other animals would believe him?"

In the classroom, your child's teacher may be teaching how to use speech marks when characters are speaking. There are many examples in this book that you could look at with your child. Find these together and point out how the end punctuation (comma, full stop, question mark or exclamation mark) comes inside the speech marks. Ask the child to read some examples out loud, adding appropriate expression.

Franklin Watts
First published in Great Britain in 2021
by The Watts Publishing Group

Series Editors: Jackie Hamley and Melanie Palmer
Series Advisors and Development Editors: Dr Sue Bodman and Glen Franklin
Series Designers: Peter Scoulding and Cathryn Gilbert

A CIP catalogue record for this book is
available from the British Library.

ISBN 978 1 4451 7696 3 (hbk)
ISBN 978 1 4451 7698 7 (pbk)
ISBN 978 1 4451 8192 9 (ebook)
ISBN 978 1 4451 7697 0 (library ebook)

Printed in China

Franklin Watts
An imprint of
Hachette Children's Group
Part of The Watts Publishing Group
Carmelite House
50 Victoria Embankment
London EC4Y 0DZ

An Hachette UK Company
www.hachette.co.uk

www.franklinwatts.co.uk

Answer to Story order: 4,1,3,5,2